Use the picture code to work out the name of an exciting holiday destination

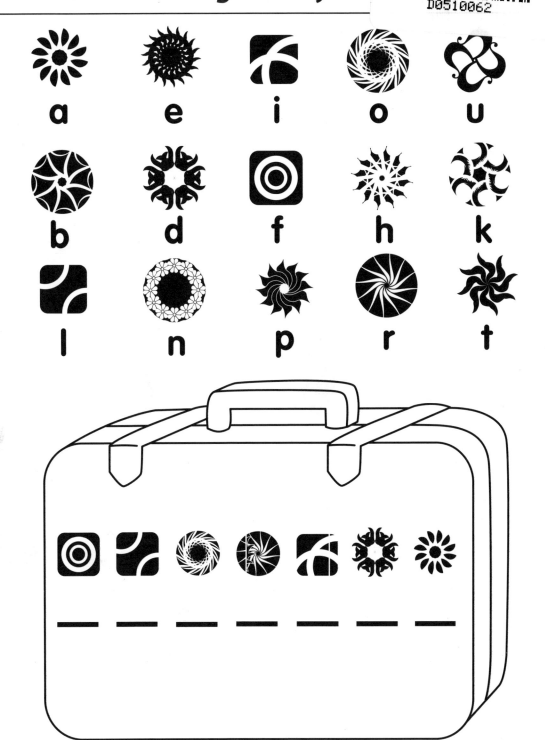

Use the clues to work out which picnic basket belongs to Rebecca.

a

e

b

f

c

g

Rebecca's basket has a handle on the top.

It doesn't have a cloth over it.

It has fruit in it.

d

h

Help Bobby find his way through the maze to the ice cream hut.

Play these games in the car.
You don't even need a pen or paper.

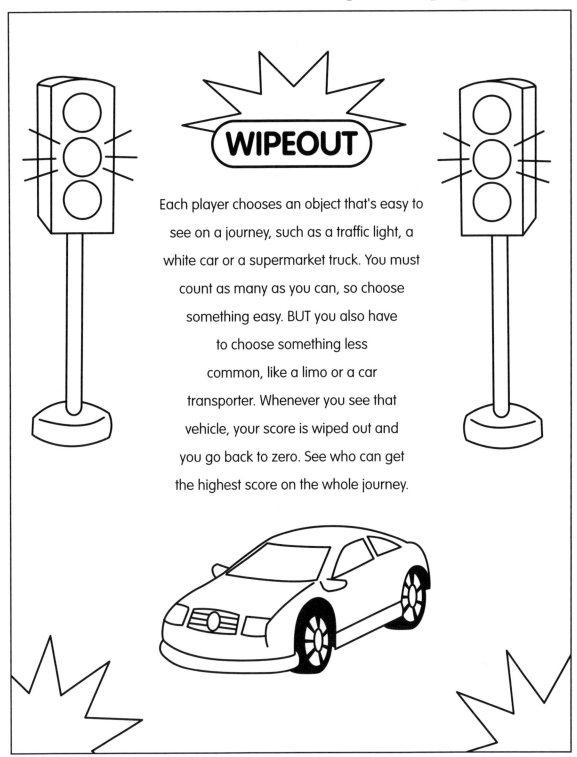

WIPEOUT

Each player chooses an object that's easy to see on a journey, such as a traffic light, a white car or a supermarket truck. You must count as many as you can, so choose something easy. BUT you also have to choose something less common, like a limo or a car transporter. Whenever you see that vehicle, your score is wiped out and you go back to zero. See who can get the highest score on the whole journey.

Are you good at map reading?
See if you can find the ancient treasure!

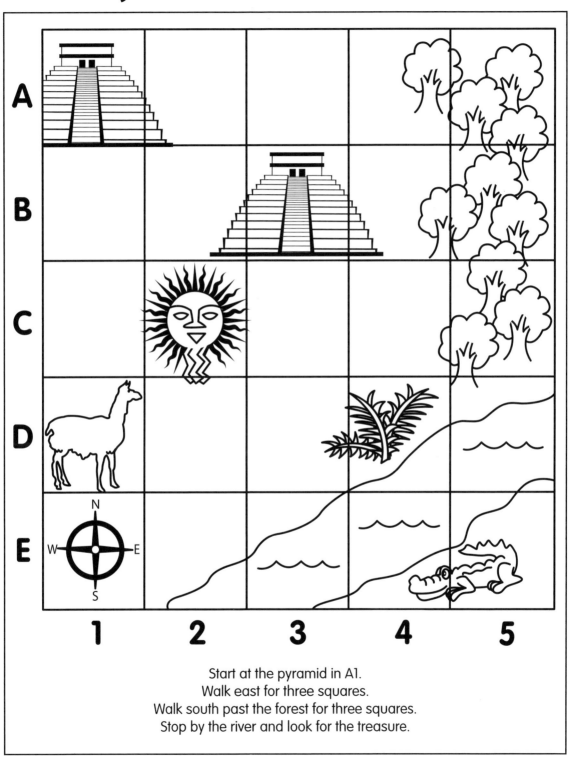

Start at the pyramid in A1.
Walk east for three squares.
Walk south past the forest for three squares.
Stop by the river and look for the treasure.

Which ticket belongs to which aeroplane?
Complete the sums to match them up.

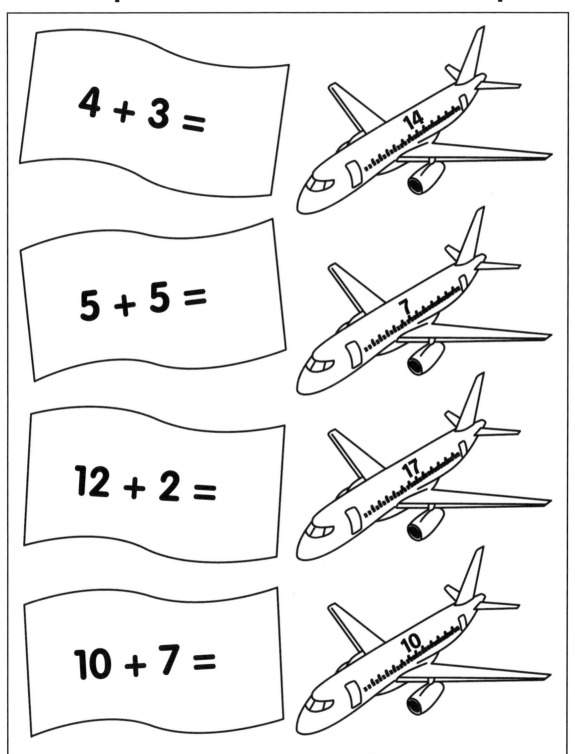

4 + 3 =

14

5 + 5 =

7

12 + 2 =

17

10 + 7 =

10

Can you spot six differences between these pictures?

Finish the picture of the sea creature.

Help the Arctic explorer find the quickest way through the ice to the North Pole.

How many planets are there on this page?
Colour them as you count them.

Play this game on the beach or in the park.
All you need is an empty lunchbox!

TREASURE HUNT

Each player needs an empty box of their own. You have ten minutes to collect as many things from the list as possible. The winner is the person with the most items.

NEVER WANDER OUT OF SIGHT OF THE GROWN UP(S) YOU ARE WITH. MAKE SURE YOU DON'T COLLECT ANYTHING SHARP, AND WASH YOUR HANDS WHEN YOU HAVE FINISHED.

Things to collect:

Smooth stone

Piece of wood

Something made of plastic

Y-shaped twig

Something green

Something with a pattern on it

Something with writing on it

A thing beginning with B

An item with a hole in

A pebble smaller than a penny

The grid has the name of six countries hidden in it. Look carefully to find them all.

```
J  C  P  H  E  T  C  D  I  Y
N  C  C  U  C  Y  P  R  U  S
X  H  A  B  S  C  J  P  C  R
H  I  Q  A  G  O  L  R  M  C
O  N  U  C  E  A  T  C  G  R
C  A  N  A  D  A  P  N  B  O
C  I  F  C  Z  K  F  C  M  A
C  L  S  L  C  S  D  U  O  T
E  C  H  I  L  E  R  B  V  I
W  R  C  K  M  G  C  A  S  A
```

CANADA
CUBA
CYPRUS
CHINA
CHILE
CROATIA

Fill in the spaces to count up in twos and fives.

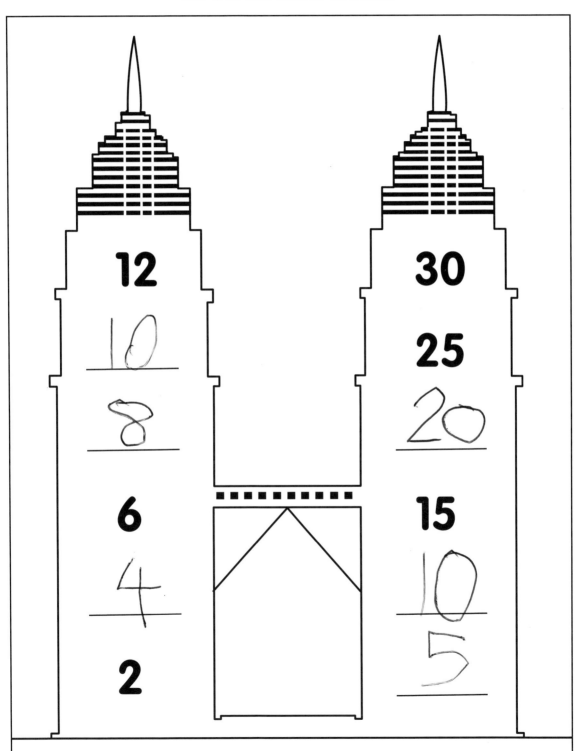

12
10
8

6
4
2

30
25
20

15
10
5

13

Draw what you'd like to eat right now.

Help the bee find a way out of the maze to the flowers.

This game is great fun on a train, plane or in a waiting room.

FUNNY FACE!

One player starts the game with the words,

"I went to Cornwall* and I pulled a face like this –"

He must make a funny face, like crossing his eyes or sucking in his cheeks. The next player repeats the words and the face of the first player, but adds her own funny face as well.

Keep on playing like that, with everybody adding on their own funny face, until someone gets the order wrong, or just can't play because they are laughing too much.

Which silhouette belongs to Ben?

Two for the price of one! See if you can solve these money puzzles.

Starting with the X, cross out every other letter to find the country where they spend Krone.

Cross out any letter that appears twice. The remaining letters spell the name of the South African currency.

Which is the quickest way to the ice cream van?

There are ten capital cities hidden in this grid. See if you can find them all.

```
K O A R L W A O V M Q B
C S P R A G U E S A P N
R T D S J Z C A I R O J
T Q X T E L B U F O U P
D S C L V O K P Y M B G
B E R L I N T B I E E O
M C N D W D V H N L I D
O H S I T O K Y O U J F
S T H M F N I E X O I Z
C M P A R I S J R G N P
O K R E Y F L Q K M G S
W G L O R M A D R I D N
```

BEIJING	MOSCOW
BERLIN	PARIS
CAIRO	PRAGUE
LONDON	ROME
MADRID	TOKYO

Draw your favourite party outfit.

You need two or more players for this outdoor game.

COOL BOULES!

Boules is a popular game in France,
but it's great fun to play wherever you are.
The name simply means "balls". If you don't have a
boules set, look for stones to play with. You need 2 larger
stones for each player, and a small stone to share.

**The first player has to throw the small stone
(the "jack") about 5 metres away. She then has
to throw one of her own stones as close
to the jack as possible.**

Take turns to throw your first stone, as close to the jack
as you can. Make sure you choose stones that are
different from each other to tell them apart, or write
your initials on them.

**Each player then throws their second stone.
The winner is the person whose stone is
closest to the jack, so throw carefully.
If you can't throw it close, try to knock
the jack or any other stones out of the way.**

Use the compass at the bottom of the map to help answer the questions.

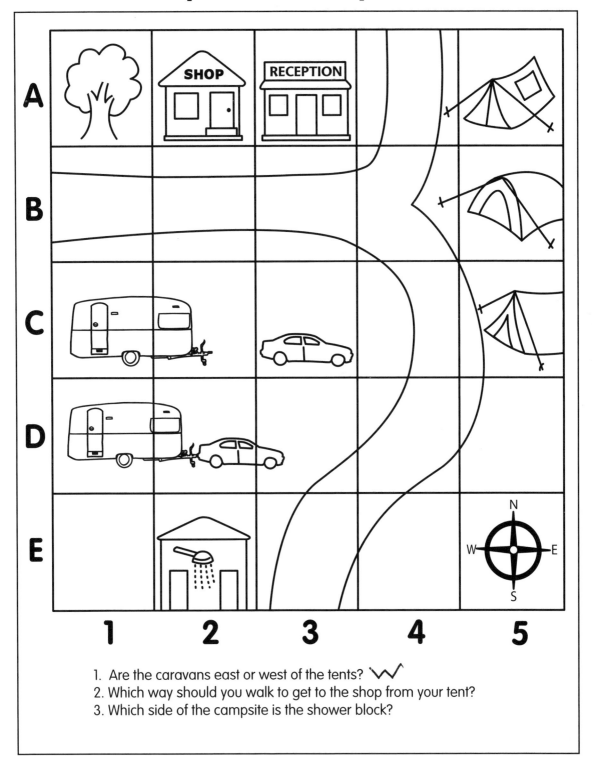

1. Are the caravans east or west of the tents? ⌄⌄
2. Which way should you walk to get to the shop from your tent?
3. Which side of the campsite is the shower block?

Sail through the maze, making sure you don't crash into any big ships on the way!

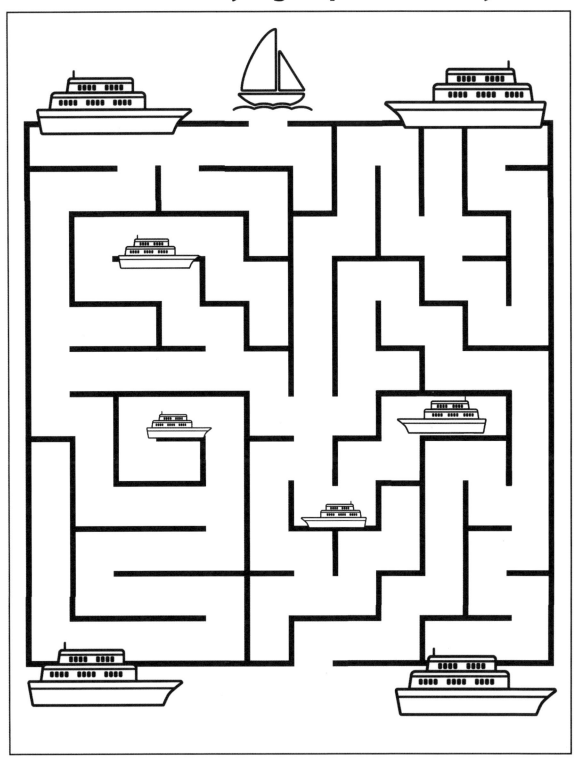

Count how many flags are jumbled up in this picture.

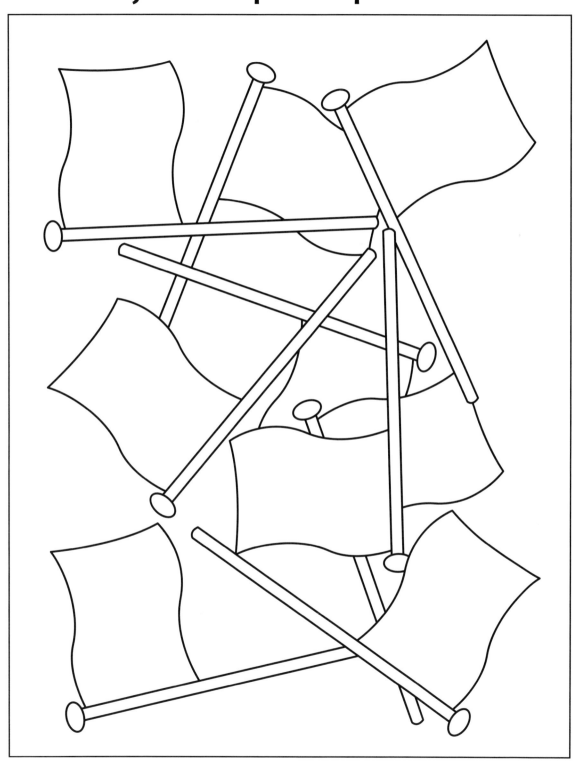

You can play this game anywhere, as long as you can see things outside.

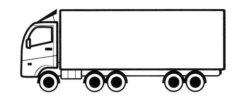

TWO BY TWO

Choose an item you can see out of the window. The other players have to spot a matching one as you travel along (like playing "Snap" with real objects). They choose an item for you to look for at the same time.

Score a point when somebody sees a chosen item, and then choose a new object for each player to stop you getting bored.

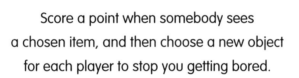

Things to spot:

Red tree

Hedge with berries

Limousine

Supermarket truck

Triangular sign

Hovering bird

Purple car

House in a field

Bike

What does Sally want to do today?
Use the clues to work it out.

Sally has no money to go shopping.
She doesn't want to see any animals.
She wants to play instead of sightseeing.
She wants to wear her new trainers!

What's that flying through the sky?

This is a great outdoor game if you have lots of people to join in.

MONSTER MASH

Draw lines in the sand, or use chalk on the ground to mark out the two banks of a river. You can spread out skipping ropes instead, if you have them.

Two players link arms to make the monster. They have to stay inside the river banks and try to catch the other players as they try to cross the river. Anyone who is caught links arms too, so the monster grows bigger and more difficult to escape from! The winner is the last player to avoid being caught.

Can you spot six differences between these pictures?

Find the ten countries hidden in the grid.

```
S  A  I  I  I  A  M  W  A  L  B  J
B  W  G  S  S  O  T  B  K  S  A
R  S  I  R  R  B  R  S  K  A  P
S  O  U  T  H  A  F  R  I  C  A
P  A  E  A  Z  E  E  A  N  C  N
C  C  S  I  F  E  G  L  D  S  M
H  H  L  A  M  O  R  O  C  C  O
I  I  S  O  U  F  R  L  G  A  R
L  N  N  A  T  S  I  K  A  P  J
S  A  N  E  C  E  E  R  G  N  A
W  A  L  E  S  I  B  R  A  Z  D
```

BRAZIL

CHINA

GREECE

ISRAEL

JAPAN

MOROCCO

PAKISTAN

SOUTH AFRICA

SWITZERLAND

WALES

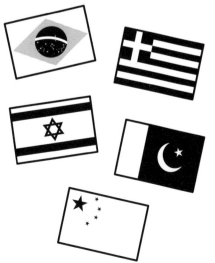

Find the quickest way past the rocks and sharks to reach the lighthouse.

Match each of the famous sights to the correct name.

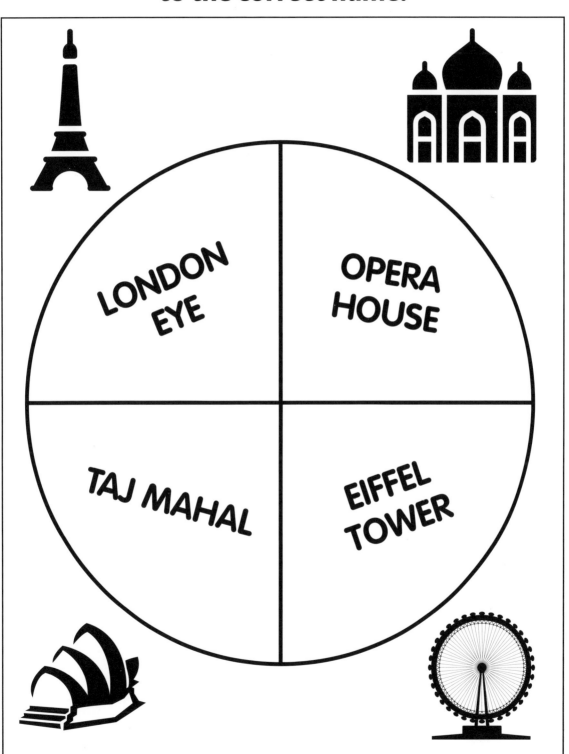

LONDON EYE

OPERA HOUSE

TAJ MAHAL

EIFFEL TOWER

Use your imagination to pass the time on a long journey.

THIS OLD MAN

You might know this rhyme already,
but it doesn't matter if you don't.
Simply say the words out loud,
or sing them if you know the tune:

This old man, he played one,

He played "nick nack" on my _____ .

With a nick, nack, paddy wack,

Give a dog a bone,

This old man came rolling home.

When you get to the
blank space, fill in a word
that rhymes with "one".

It can be serious or
downright silly, it's
up to you!

Sing the song again and
again, counting up each time.

Which skateboard belongs to Louie?

Colour in the peacock to make it even more spectacular.

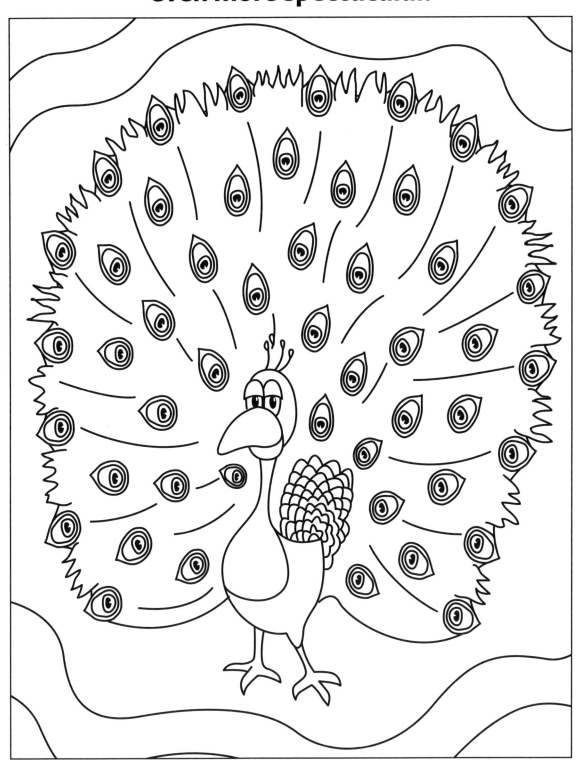

Set sail to see which of the islands is suitable for your holiday.

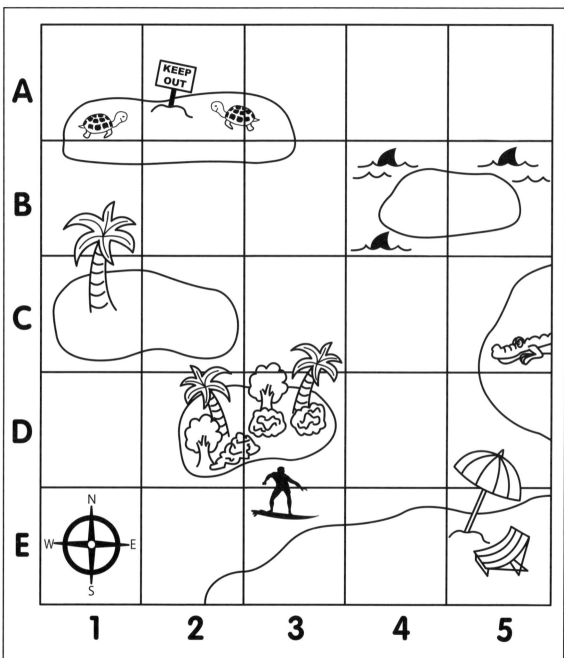

Sail due north from Surfer's Beach in E4. Do you reach a safe island?

Sail northwest for one square. Can you stay on this island?

Sail directly south for two squares. Is this island any good?

Which squares would you visit to find a better island?

Can you find 12 seaside words hidden in the grid? All of them begin with S.

```
S  E  L  T  S  A  C  D  N  A  S
S  U  S  A  N  D  A  L  S  S  T
H  E  E  S  U  S  U  G  W  U  A
O  C  A  S  S  E  T  S  I  N  R
R  P  G  W  A  H  S  A  M  B  F
E  I  U  S  E  N  E  N  S  L  I
L  J  L  D  U  E  A  D  U  O  S
L  M  L  S  A  N  D  W  I  C  H
E  K  S  S  U  N  H  A  T  K  S
H  R  S  A  N  S  P  A  D  E  E
S  U  D  R  A  P  B  F  T  Z  G
```

SEAWEED   SWIMSUIT

SUNHAT   SANDWICH

SEAGULL   SANDALS

SHORE   STARFISH

SPADE   SANDCASTLE

SHELL   SUNBLOCK

HINT! Some words are hidden
backwards or diagonally.

This game is great for a sunny day at the beach or in the garden.

WET AND WILD

The rules to this game are simple, but it's fantastic fun. All you need are some water bomb balloons. Fill them quite full and ask an adult to tie the ends.

Stand in a circle and throw the water bomb from player to player. Make sure you catch the bomb or you will get splashed. You also have to be careful how you catch it. If you squeeze it too hard it will burst all over you!

If it's too easy, shout out a name as you throw the bomb – but don't always shout the name of the person you are throwing to! Make the game more fun (and splashy) by throwing the water bombs high in the air, or throw more than one water bomb around the circle.

SPLASH!

Use the picture clues to fill in the answers in the crossword grid.

ACROSS

1.

3.

7.

8.

9.

11.

14.

15.

16.

17.

DOWN

1.

2.

4.

5.

6.

10.

11.

12.

13.

Count down from 10 to get through the water park to the wave pool.

Only two of these snakes have matching patterns. Can you see which two?

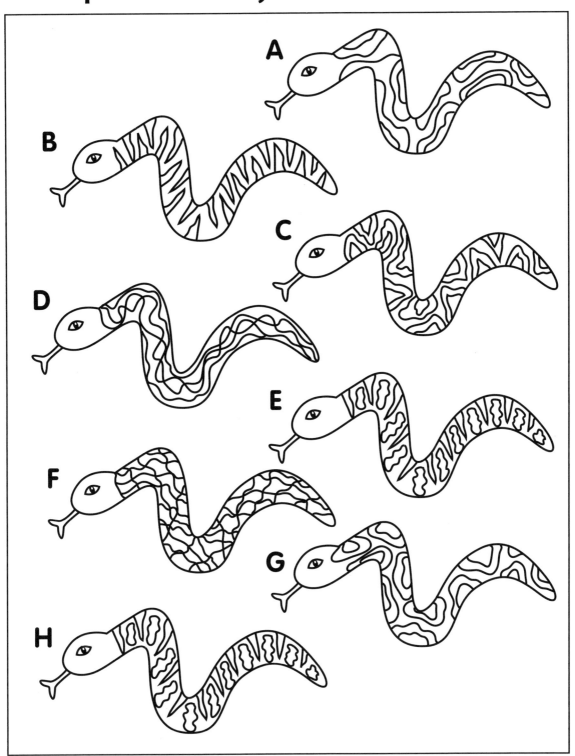

Here's a game to test your brainpower when you're stuck in a vehicle for ages.

RHYME TIME

One player goes first and says a word out loud. It can be any simple word, like 'house' or 'train'.

Every other player takes a turn to say a word that rhymes. Score a point if you think of a proper rhyme that no one has said before. Lose a point if you shout out when it isn't your turn, or if you say a nonsense word or repeat someone else's word.

When all the rhyming words have been said, let someone else choose a word.

See who can be the first player to score 25 points.

FRIES

What's growing in the garden?

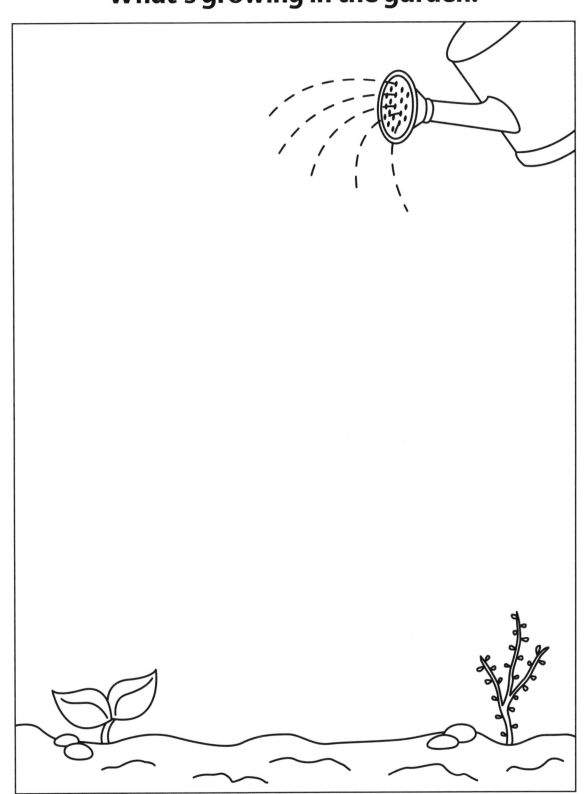

This game needs a big space to play it in! Run around outside so you don't break anything.

BIG FOOT

Divide the players into two teams. You can play with just two people if that's all you have. Each team needs a pair of really BIG shoes or swimming flippers.

Make a starting line and a finish line. Draw them in the sand or with chalk or pebbles. Put the Big Foot shoes on the starting line in front of each team or player.

Start when someone says "Go!" Put on the Big Foot shoes and race towards the finish line. Turn around and run back again. Be careful that you don't fall and hurt yourself. If you lose a shoe you have to stop and put it back on before you can carry on racing.

If you're playing in teams, take it in turns to wear the Big Foot shoes and race to the finish line and back again. The winner is, of course, the team that finishes first.

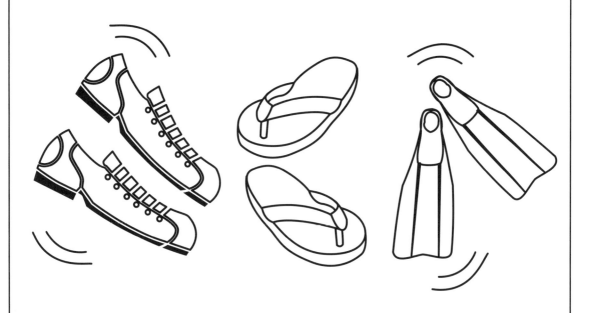

One of these frogs is a little bit different from the others. See if you can spot which it is.

Use the grid references to answer the questions about this farm.

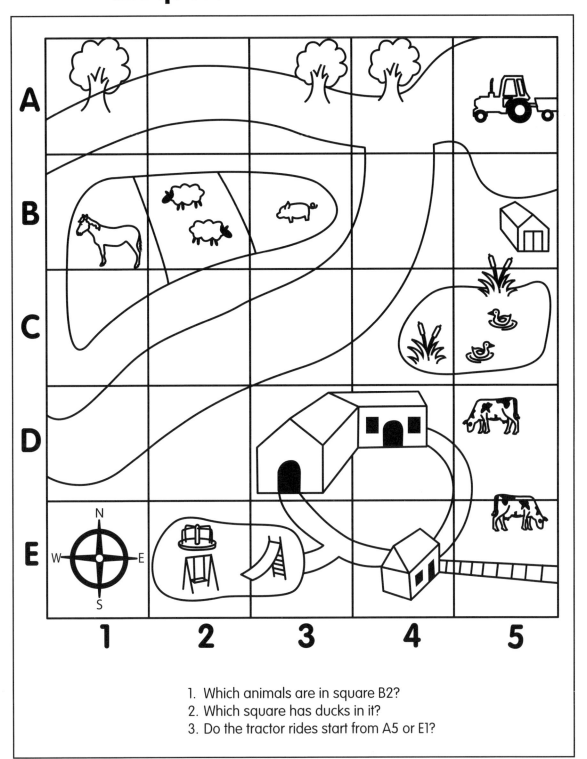

1. Which animals are in square B2?
2. Which square has ducks in it?
3. Do the tractor rides start from A5 or E1?

Don't get bored on a long journey — get brainier!

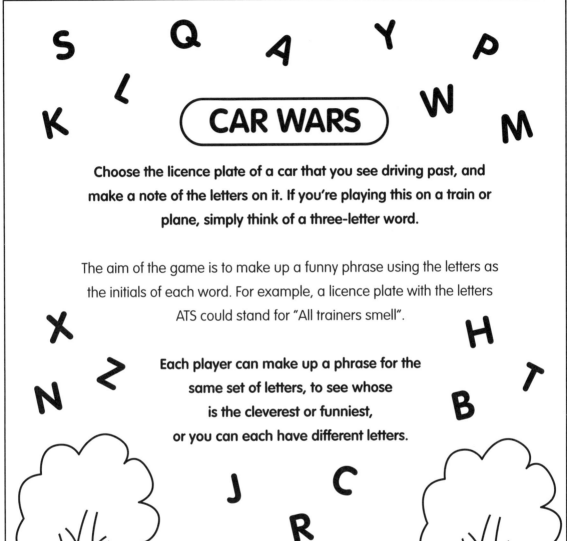

CAR WARS

Choose the licence plate of a car that you see driving past, and make a note of the letters on it. If you're playing this on a train or plane, simply think of a three-letter word.

The aim of the game is to make up a funny phrase using the letters as the initials of each word. For example, a licence plate with the letters ATS could stand for "All trainers smell".

Each player can make up a phrase for the same set of letters, to see whose is the cleverest or funniest, or you can each have different letters.

Can you identify the six vehicles and find their names in the grid?

```
G F P L A N E X M K
O T W T S G M I O H
E S C D E M V H T P
P N B N R F R Q O G
H Q I V E B C A R B
D L C B H I C N B O
J V Y H T C R U I L
C I C K Y L S J K T
H E L I C O P T E R
Z K E B O A T K A U
```

Gather together as many players as you can to make this outdoor game even more fun.

WHAT TIME IS IT?

Choose one player to be "It". In this game he is known as Mr Wolf. He stands about 10 metres from the other players, with his back turned.

The players all shout, "**What time is it, Mr Wolf?**" He answers with any time he likes, for example, "**Eight o'clock!**" The players must take eight steps towards him. If he turns around to look at them, they must instantly freeze until he turns away again.

Carry on asking the time until Mr Wolf answers,

"Dinner time!"

Or someone gets close enough to tap him on the shoulder.

Then Mr Wolf has to chase everyone back to the start line. If he catches someone, it is their turn to be Mr Wolf.

Colour in this crazy clown!

Help Robbie find his way through the maze to the picnic basket waiting in the middle.

Use the compass at the top of the map to help answer the questions.

1. Is the mosque in the north or south of the town?

2. Which side of the town is the castle?

3. Do you walk north or south from the fountain to get to the station?

You need pens and paper to play this simple travelling game.

THE NAME GAME

You can play this game on your own. Write the letters of your name down the side of your paper. The aim of the game is to spot something that begins with each letter. So if your name is Cody, you will be looking for a cat, an orange car, a daffodil and so on. Write down each item as you spot it.

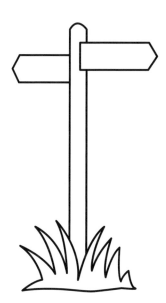

When you have finished, choose another name and try again. If you want to play with a friend, you should both use the same name and have a race to see who finishes first.

Study the parrots carefully and then answer the question.

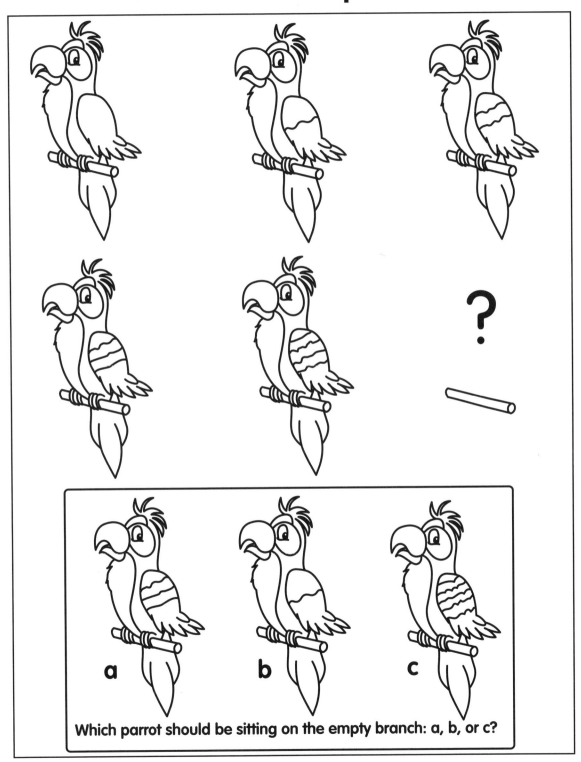

Which parrot should be sitting on the empty branch: a, b, or c?

Look at the names on the page.
Draw an oval around the rivers and
a rectangle around the cities.

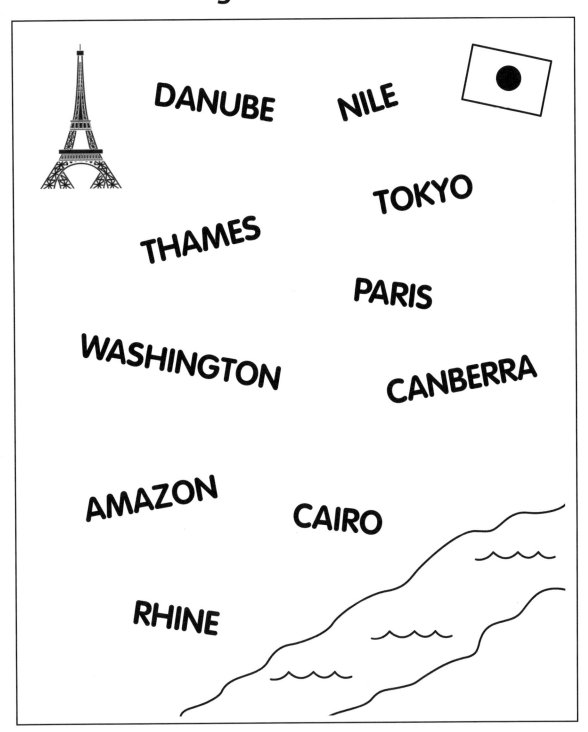

DANUBE   NILE

TOKYO

THAMES

PARIS

WASHINGTON   CANBERRA

AMAZON   CAIRO

RHINE

Find a matching partner for each of the lighthouses.

Which picture of the Leaning Tower of Pisa is the odd one out?

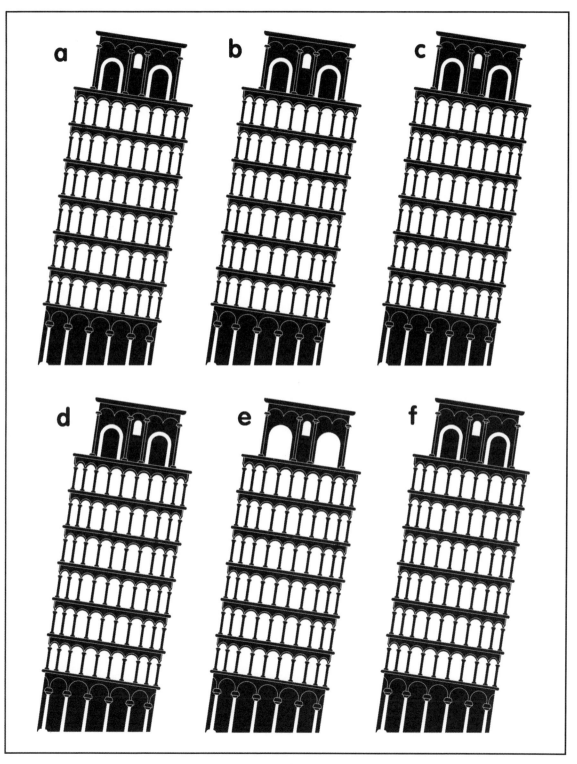

Follow the arrows to guide the frog prince across the pond, without jumping on any other frogs.

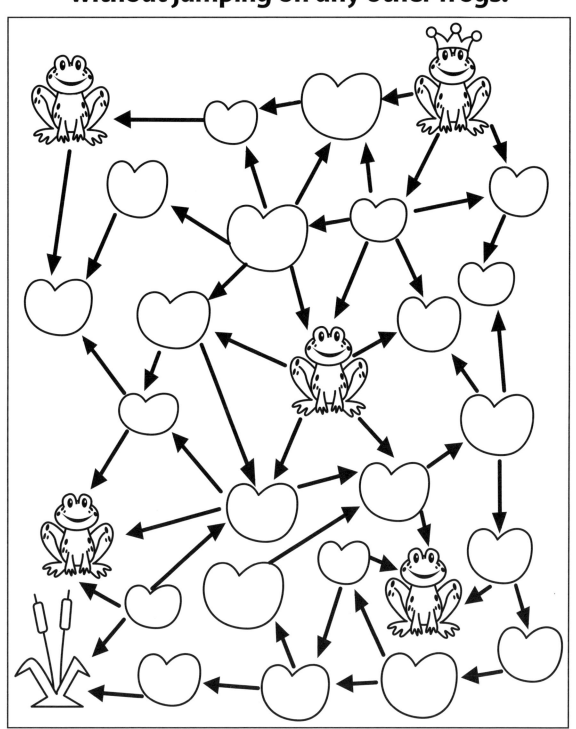

You can play this game in restaurants, waiting rooms and on the move, it's so simple.

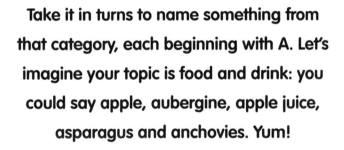

A TO Z

One player chooses a category. Think of subjects all of your players know a little about, such as animals, countries, sporting words or food and drink.

Take it in turns to name something from that category, each beginning with A. Let's imagine your topic is food and drink: you could say apple, aubergine, apple juice, asparagus and anchovies. Yum!

When every player has said something, without repeating a word that has already been chosen, move on to B. Let the next player in the playing order go first (otherwise the same person always speaks last and the game is much harder for them).

Help the crab scuttle through the maze to reach the beach at the bottom.

Finish the picture of the alien.

How many times can you count the word SUN and RAIN in the grids?

```
      S S   U U
    N S S U N U
  S S U N N S S U
  U S N U N N S U
  S S U N U S U S
  U N S U N U N U
    S N S N N S
      U S N S
```

```
  A N R A I N R A R
  S R A N R N N R A R
R S R A I N I A R A I A R
R R A I N R A I N I N I A
  I N N A R R A I N I N
```

63

Use the grid references to answer the questions about the map of the museum.

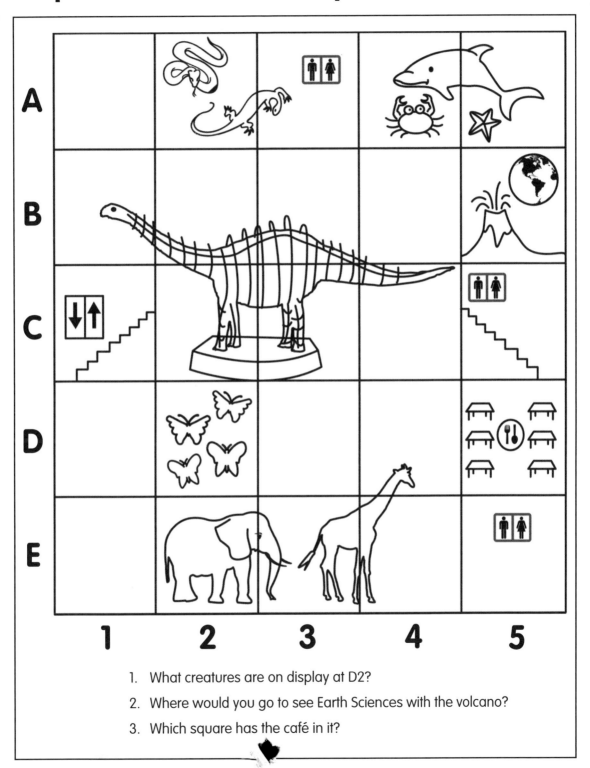

1. What creatures are on display at D2?
2. Where would you go to see Earth Sciences with the volcano?
3. Which square has the café in it?

Use the price labels to answer the questions in the 'Around the World' souvenir shop.

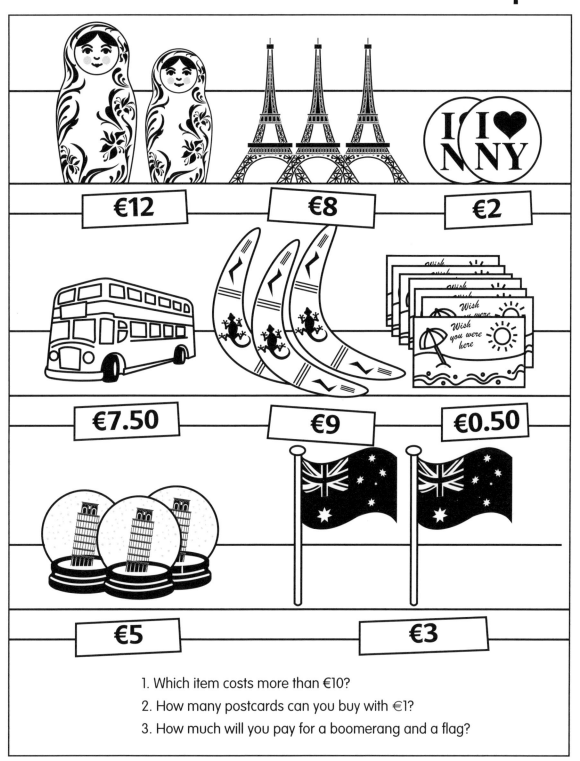

€12

€8

€2

€7.50

€9

€0.50

€5

€3

1. Which item costs more than €10?

2. How many postcards can you buy with €1?

3. How much will you pay for a boomerang and a flag?

Can you spot six differences between these two pictures?

Find a wide open space to run around with your friends.

STUCK IN THE MUD

This game is best with lots of players.
One person is **It** and has to try to catch the others.
(If there are more than ten players,
choose two people to be **It**.)

Any player who is caught has to stand still with their
legs spread apart. They cannot move until another
free player crawls between their legs to
release them. Of course, it's easier for **It** to catch
a player if she is crawling through someone's
legs, so watch out!

Take turns to be **It** so that
nobody gets bored of
always having to chase
the others.

Look carefully at the scene, then work out which overhead picture matches it exactly.

a

b

c

d

How many different words can you make out of AROUND THE WORLD?

UNDER

RED

Add your own colour to this cool character.

Find a way back to the tents from the shower block.

Use the clues to work out which skateboard belongs to Joe.

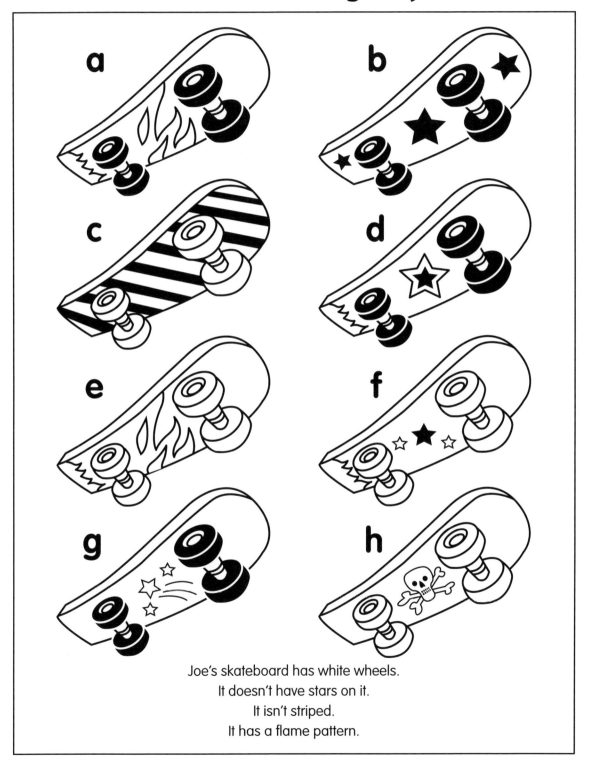

a

b

c

d

e

f

g

h

Joe's skateboard has white wheels.

It doesn't have stars on it.

It isn't striped.

It has a flame pattern.

Use the clues to change one word into another word, changing one letter each time.

W A L K

— — — — Speak to someone

— — — — Another word for a story

— — — — Bathroom wall covering

— — — — When the sea covers the beach

R I D E

Answers

1. Florida

2. Basket e

3.

5. The treasure is in the plants in D4.

6. 4 + 3 = 7
   5 + 5 = 10
   12 + 2 = 14
   10 + 7 = 17

7.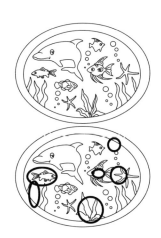

9.

10. There are 8 planets.

12.

```
J C P H E T C D I Y
N C C U C Y P R U S
X H A B S C J P C M S R
X Q A G O L T R C R O
O N U C E A T P R C R O
C A N A D A P F N G B M O A
C I F C Z K F C B M O V T
C L S L C S D U O V
E C H I L E R B V S A
W R C K M G C A S A
```

(13.)

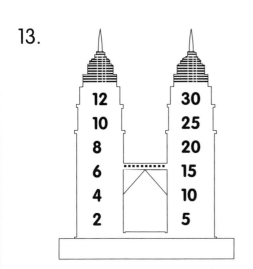

```
12    30
10    25
 8    20
 6    15
 4    10
 2     5
```

15.

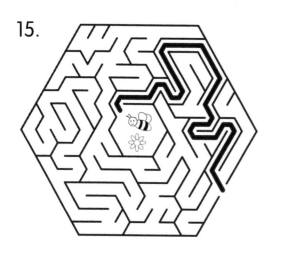

17. Silhouette e

18. They spend Krone in Denmark.
The South African currency is the Rand.

19.

20.

```
K O A R L W A O V M Q B
C S P R A G U E S A P N
R T D S J Z C A I R O J
T Q X T E L B U F O U P
D S C L V O K P Y M B G
B E R L I N T B I E O D
M C N D W D V H N L O D
O H S I T O K Y O L U J F
S T H M F N I E X O Z
C M P A R I S J R G N P
O K R E Y F L Q K M G S
W G L O R M A D R I D N
```

23. West
West
South

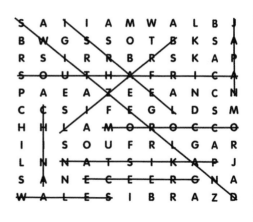

24.

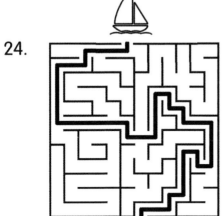

25. 9 flags

27. Sally wants to go to the playground.

30.

31.

32.

33. EIFFEL TOWER

TAJ MAHAL

LONDON EYE

OPERA HOUSE

35.

40.

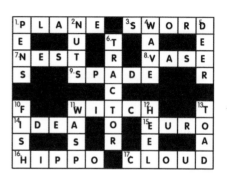

¹P	L	A	²N	E		³S	⁴W	O	R	⁵D
E			U		⁶T		A			E
⁷N	E	S	T		R		⁸V	A	S	E
S			⁹S	P	A	D	E			R
					C					
¹⁰F			¹¹W	I	T	C	¹²H			¹³T
¹⁴I	D	E	A		O		¹⁵E	U	R	O
S			S		R		E			A
¹⁶H	I	P	P	O		¹⁷C	L	O	U	D

41.

37. No, it has too many sharks.
No, it is for turtles laying eggs.
No, it is too overgrown.
The best island is in C1 and C2.

38.

42. E and H

46. C

47. 1. Sheep
2. C5
3. A5

49.

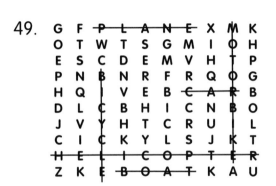

```
G  F  P  L  A  N  E  X  M  K
O  T  W  T  S  G  M  I  O  H
E  S  C  D  E  M  V  H  T  P
P  N  B  N  R  F  R  Q  O  G
H  Q  I  V  E  B  C  A  R  B
D  L  C  B  H  I  C  N  B  O
J  V  Y  H  T  C  R  U  I  L
C  I  C  K  Y  L  S  J  K  T
H  E  L  I  C  O  P  T  E  R
Z  K  E  B  O  A  T  K  A  U
```

BICYCLE   HELICOPTER

CAR   PLANE

MOTORBIKE BOAT

52.

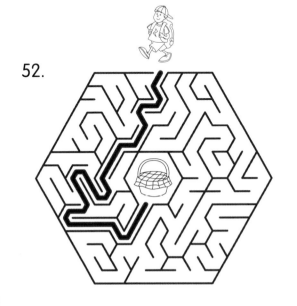

53. 1. North

   2. East

   3. South

55. c

56. Danube, Nile, Thames, Amazon and Rhine are all rivers.

Tokyo, Paris, Washington, Canberra and Cairo are cities.

57. 1 is the same as 7

   2 is the same as 8

   3 is the same as 5

   4 is the same as 6

58. e

59.

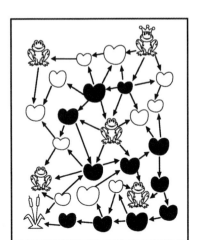

63.

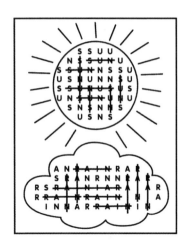

SUN appears 10 times
RAIN appears 11 times

61.

64. 1. Butterflies
2. B5
3. D5

65. 1. Russian dolls
2. 2 postcards
3. €12

66.

71.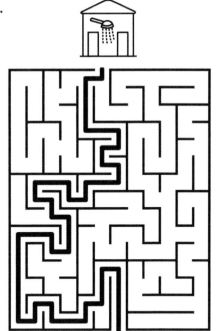

68. c

69. Here are just a few:

NEW

WON

DRAW

OLD

DOWN

REAL

THROW

RETURN

HOWLER

but there are lots!

72. e

73. WALK

TALK

TALE

TILE

TIDE

RIDE